Garfield

Two's Company

JIM DAVIS

Ravette Limited

This edition first published by
Ravette Limited 1984

Printed and bound in Great Britain
for Ravette Limited,
12 Star Road, Partridge Green,
Horsham, Sussex RH13 8RA
by Richard Clay (The Chaucer Press) Ltd,
Bungay, Suffolk

ISBN 0 906710 50 2

© 1983 United Feature Syndicate, Inc.

8-31

THIS IS MY HUMBLE ABODE, MY DEAR

JIM DAVIS 1-20

© 1983 United Feature Syndicate, Inc.

WHO WERE THEY?

OH, JUST A COUPLE OF ANIMALS I'M GIVING AWAY SOON

JIM DAVIS 9-30

1-12   JIM DAVIS

GARFIELD, YOU SEEM TO BE PREOCCUPIED THIS WEEK

HUH?

© 1983 United Feature Syndicate, Inc.

© 1983 United Feature Syndicate, Inc.

12-20

© 1983 United Feature Syndicate, Inc.

© 1983 United Feature Syndicate, Inc.

© 1983 United Feature Syndicate, Inc.

© 1983 United Feature Syndicate, Inc.

© 1983 United Feature Syndicate, Inc.

© 1982 United Feature Syndicate, Inc.

JIM DAVIS

12-3

CLANG!

HEY, GARFIELD, HOW DO YOU LIKE MY NEW DINNER BELL?

© 1983 United Feature Syndicate, Inc.

IT GOT MY ATTENTION

© 1983 United Feature Syndicate, Inc.

© 1983 United Feature Syndicate, Inc.

© 1983 United Feature Syndicate, Inc.

© 1983 United Feature Syndicate, Inc.

THE CAPTAIN HAS ADVISED
THAT THE "FASTEN SEAT BELT"
SIGN BE OBSERVED IN CASE
SOME SLIGHT AIR TURBULENCE
IS ENCOUNTERED

© 1983 United Feature Syndicate, Inc.

© 1983 United Feature Syndicate, In

© 1983 United Feature Syndicate, Inc.

© 1983 United Feature Syndicate, Inc.

© 1983 United Feature Syndicate, Inc.

NICE TRY, GARFIELD,
BUT I DON'T BUY YOUR
STUPID WATERMELON
DISGUISE

RATA TATTA
TATTA TATA

HEY, GARFIELD, WHEN WAS THE LAST TIME YOU SAW MY PET FROG, HERBIE?

SNAK!

AT LUNCH

© 1983 United Feature Syndicate, Inc.

© 1983 United Feature Syndicate, Inc.

© 1983 United Feature Syndicate, Inc.

GARFIELD, I KNOW BEING A CAT OWNER IS A BIG RESPONSIBILITY

BUT I SHOULD BE ABLE TO LEAVE FOR AN EVENING WITHOUT YOU DESTROYING EVERYTHING!

I WANT A DIVORCE!

I GET HALF OF EVERYTHING

6-2

SLAM

1-10

JIM DAVIS

HEY, GARFIELD.
I'M HOME

YOU'RE CERTAINLY
EXCITED TO SEE ME

BELIEVE ME,
INSIDE I'M HOPPING
UP AND DOWN
AND SHOUTING
WITH GLEE

© 1983 United Feature Syndicate, Inc.

© 1983 United Feature Syndicate, Inc.

© 1983 United Feature Syndicate, Inc.

JIM DAVIS   11-19

STOP PLAYING
WITH YOUR FOOD,
GARFIELD

© 1983 United Feature Syndicate, Inc.

I'M NOT.
IT DRIED OUT
WHILE MY
FACE WAS
IN IT

WELL, WHAT DID YOU THINK OF THE MAN-EATING LION MOVIE?

2-19

YOU KNOW I HATE THAT, GARFIELD

© 1983 United Feature Syndicate, Inc.

© 1983 United Feature Syndicate, Inc.

HA-HA! YOU DIDN'T GET MY FOOD THAT TIME!

SPLAT!

© 1983 United Feature Syndicate, Inc.

© 1983 United Feature Syndicate, Inc.

7-19

© 1983 United Feature Syndicate, Inc.

IM DAVIS

9-2

© 1983 United Feature Syndicate, Inc.

OTHER GARFIELD BOOKS IN THIS SERIES

All these books are available at your local bookshop or newsagent, or can be ordered direct from the publisher. Just tick the titles you require and fill in the form below.

Prices and availability subject to change without notice.

Ravette Limited, 12 Star Road, Partridge Green, Horsham, West Sussex RH13 8RA

Please send cheque or postal order, and allow the following for postage and packing. U.K. 45p for one book, plus 20p for the second and 14p for each additional book ordered up to a £1.63 maximum.

Name..

Address..

....